It's Another Ace Book from CGP

This book is for 14-16 year olds.

First we stick in all the _really important Physical Geography stuff_ you need to do well in the GCSE Geography Exam.

Then we have a really good stab at making it funny — so you'll _actually use it_.

Simple as that.

CGP are just the best

The central aim of Coordination Group Publications is to produce top quality books that are carefully written, immaculately presented and marvellously funny — whilst always making sure they exactly cover the National Curriculum for each subject.

And then we supply them to as many people as we possibly can, as _cheaply_ as we possibly can.

Buy our books — they're ace

Contents

Section Six — Weather and Climate

Section Seven — Ecosystems and Soils

Section Eight — Maps

Section Nine — Answers 78

Published by Coordination Group Publications Ltd.
Additional Illustrations by: Lex Ward

Contributors:
Eileen Worthington BSc (Hons) PGCE
Charley Darbishire BA (Hons)
Chris Dennett BSc (Hons)
Dominic Hall BSc (Hons)
Andy Park BSc (Hons)
Claire Thompson BSc
James Paul Wallis BEng (Hons)

With Thanks to:
Magda Halsall MA (Hons) MA(Econ) PGCE for the proof reading.

ISBN 1 84146 702 2

Groovy website: www.cgpbooks.co.uk

Printed by Elanders Hindson, Newcastle upon Tyne.

Plate Tectonics

The parts of the earth and how they move might seem a bit boring. But if you don't know about that you'll never understand earthquakes, volcanoes, the meaning of life...

Q1.   Answer the following:

   a) The outer layer of the Earth is made up of large "jigsaw-like pieces". What are these called?

   ....

   b) What causes them to move?   ....

   c) How much do they move per year? A few mm or a few metres?

   ....

   d) What is the name for the zones/lines where they meet?

   ....

Bill couldn't help thinking
his new jigsaw was too tricky.

Q2.   Label the following diagrams with the name of the type
       of plate margin shown. Give an example for each one.

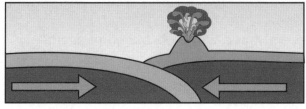

   a) ....
   eg ....

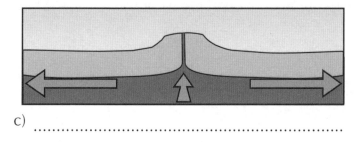

   c) ....
   eg ....

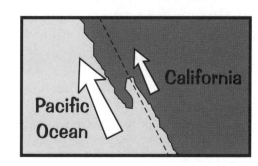

   b) ....
   eg ....

Q3.   What do we call the type of mountains formed in Q2a?

   ....

Tectonictastic...

Are you going to San Francisco... no chance mate.

This plate tectonics stuff isn't just history — it's happening all the time. One day there's going to be one hell of an earthquake along that San Andreas fault and I for one <u>don't</u> intend to be there.

Volcanoes

Steam, smoke, gas... and that's just your ears.
But don't worry — these great volcano questions will sort you right out — enjoy.

Q1.   Give brief answers to the following:

a) What is the name for a volcano that's very old, and has never erupted in recorded history?

....

b) Name an example.

....

c) What is the name for a volcano which is "sleeping", and may erupt again?

....

d) Name an example.

....

e) What do we call a volcano that's erupted recently, and will probably erupt again?

....

f) Name an example.

....

g) Approximately how many active volcanoes are there around the world?

....

h) What is the name of the area around the Pacific Ocean, which has many of the world's volcanoes?

....

i) Name the two types of plate boundary where volcanoes are found.

1 ....

2 ....

Volcanoes

Q2.   Label this diagram of a <u>composite volcano</u>:

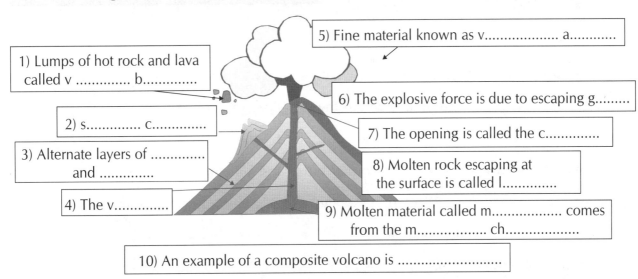

1) Lumps of hot rock and lava
   called v .... b..............

2) s............. c..............

3) Alternate layers of ....
   and ....

4) The v.............

5) Fine material known as v.................. a.............

6) The explosive force is due to escaping g.........

7) The opening is called the c.............

8) Molten rock escaping at
   the surface is called l.............

9) Molten material called m................. comes
   from the m................. ch..................

10) An example of a composite volcano is ....

Q3.   These are mixed-up descriptions of <u>shield</u> and <u>dome volcanoes</u>.
       Put them in the table at the bottom under the right heading.

Lava is acid.   Lava is runny.   Lava flows slowly and hardens quickly.

eg MT St. Helens, USA.

The volcano that forms is a large, wide, flat mountain.

Lava flows quickly and takes longer to harden.

Lava is basic.   eg Mauna Loa in Hawaii.   Lava is thicker.

The volcano that forms is therefore a steep-sided dome shape.

Shield volcano	Dome volcano

Earthquakes, volcanoes, global apocalypse — or just Geog Sec 1...

Volcanoes are pretty interesting stuff I reckon. All that exploding gas and spurting lava and flying
rocks... Anyway, if you can answer <u>all</u> these questions, you're up to speed on everything you
need to know — and if you can't... go back to that beautiful CGP revision book.

Earthquakes

Is that an earthquake? Oh no, its just the stampede of students rushing to answer these earthquake questions. That's probably because earthquakes are important in the exam.

Q1.   Fill in the gaps in this paragraph about earthquakes:

Earthquakes occur at plate boundaries, where shock waves known as .... waves suddenly occur. The place where the shock waves start is the ...., and the first place on the Earth's surface to be hit by the waves is the .... The amount the ground shakes is recorded by an instrument called a .... The size or m .... of an earthquake is given a number from the R .... Scale. Numbers 1 and 2 mean a gentle earthquake, and 7 and 8 mean strong earthquakes that can cause a lot of death and destruction. Each number on this scale is .... times bigger than the previous number.

Q2.   From this list, circle the three places where people are most at risk from earthquakes:

JAPAN   BRITAIN   CALIFORNIA   HOLLAND   MEXICO

Q3.   Write a brief explanation of <u>each</u> of these statements:

a) In residential areas, more deaths occur if an earthquake strikes at night than during the day.

....

....

b) In LEDCs, such as India, earthquakes have a higher death toll than in MEDCs.

....

....

c) Earthquakes in California (eg Los Angeles 1994) cause lots of very expensive damage.

....

....

d) An earthquake in Alaska is less of a hazard to people than one in California.

....

....

Surviving Tectonic Hazards

These days Examiners really want to know about how tectonic hazards affect people.
If *they* really want to know about it — then *you* really want to know about it too.

Q1.   Give short answers to these questions:

a) Why do people live near (and even on) volcanoes, despite the risk of an eruption,
eg Mt Etna in Sicily?

....

....

b) Why do people live in earthquake zones, despite the risk, eg California?

....

....

Q2.   "Hazard management" means doing things to predict and prepare for a hazard and doing
things to cope with a disaster if it occurs. Answer the following about hazard management:

a) Describe four ways in which people attempt to <u>predict</u> tectonic hazards.

....

....

....

....

....

....

b) Describe six ways that people can plan and be prepared,
in case there's a disaster from an earthquake or volcanic eruption.

....

....

....

....

....

....

....

....

Surviving Tectonic Hazards

Q3.   Finish off these sentences to describe how people in MEDCs
      (such as the USA) cope immediately <u>after</u> an earthquake or eruption.

1.   Experts assess ....
....

2.   Local people are told ....
....

3.   The injured are ....
....

4.   Services like power, clean water and sewage disposal must be ....
     .... because ....
....

5.   Communications (roads, phone, rail) must be ....
because ....
....

Q4.   Write down (in full sentences) <u>ten</u> reasons why tectonic hazards are
      more of a problem in LEDCs than in MEDCs. Include examples.

....
....
....
....
....
....
....
....
....
....

<u>Tectonics Martinis — shaken not stirred...</u>

Grey is the new black, white is the new grey, and stuff like this is the new physical geography.
It's no good knowing about earthquakes and volcanoes unless you know how they affect people,
how people manage these hazards and how the problems vary between LEDCs and MEDCs. Ace.

Rock Types

Some people get very excited about wandering around, looking at different rock types — and some people are normal. It may not be interesting but you've gotta learn it, so have a look at these questions.

Q1. Answer the following:

a) Name the three types (classes) of rocks.

....

b) What are igneous rocks made of?

....

c) Write a brief definition of "intrusive igneous rocks", and name one example.

....

....

d) Write a brief definition of "extrusive igneous rocks", and name one example.

....

....

e) Label the features on the diagram which start with the letters S, D, V, and B.

Put I or E against each one, showing whether the rock is intrusive or extrusive.

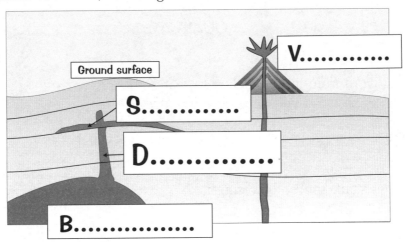

Q2. Correct this paragraph by circling the correct word in each of the pairs:

SEDIMENTARY ROCKS are made of particles, in layers. These layers are called sheets/beds. Particles of sand eroded from the land by water and wind are deposited/destroyed in the sea. Layers build up and become hardened to form a rock called sandstone/basalt. In a similar way, eroded particles of clay become layers of clay or chalk/shale. The proper name for the layers is strata/joints, and each layer is separated from the next by a floodplain/bedding plane. Limestone and chalk are sedimentary rocks made of layers of lava/calcium carbonate, which comes from the eroded remains of microskeletons and sills/shells. Another sedimentary rock is coal, made from the remains of plants/animals.

Rock Types

Q3. Explain briefly how METAMORPHIC ROCKS form.

....

....

Q4. State three ways that metamorphic rocks are different from the rocks they are formed from.

....

....

....

Q5. Draw lines to match the metamorphic rocks to the rocks they formed from:

SANDSTONE   MARBLE

LIMESTONE   GNEISS

GRANITE   SLATE

CLAY   QUARTZITE

Q6. Choose the correct word from the list below to match the descriptions given. Each word will be used only once.

CLAY   GRANITE   METAMORPHIC ROCKS   SANDSTONE

a) These rocks form resistant, spectacular crags:

....

b) This igneous rock forms moorland and tors:

....

Wow, spectacular crags

c) Valleys are eroded easily in this soft sedimentary rock:

....

d) Moorlands with sandy soils like Exmoor are made from this sedimentary rock:

....

Rock Types

Q7. Large areas of Britain consist of limestone and chalk upland areas.

a) Name an area of limestone upland.

....

b) Name an area of chalk upland.

....

c) "Limestone is pervious to rainwater." Give a brief explanation of what this means.

....

....

d) "Chalk is porous to rainwater." Briefly explain what this means.

....

....

e) What are there not many of in limestone and chalk areas, as a result of c) and d)?

....

Q8. Escarpments form where the <u>strata</u> of limestone or chalk are tilted. What is the other name for an escarpment?

....

Q9. Fill in the labels to complete this diagram of an escarpment:

The s.......... slope

The d.......... slope

Clay

Water often flows out of the ground here as a s.............

This rock is c.........
or l......................

Scared of rocks — be a little boulder...
There's a great limestone pavement near Settle in Yorkshire.

<u>Weathering</u>

Here we go with the really exciting stuff. Weathering comes in a number of different types
and you need to learn about them all. I bet you can barely contain your excitement...

Q1.   Give a brief definition of the word "weathering".

....

....

Q2.   The coloured words in this paragraph are <u>wrong</u>. Write the correct versions in the spaces:

<u>Physical weathering: Freeze–thaw action in temperate climates.</u>
In climates like Britain's, it can be around freezing point (30°C/..........) in summer/
.... at night. Soup/ .... can be trapped in cracks in rocks, and when
this freezes, it contracts/ .... By day, this melts and expands/ ....
This can happen over and over again, strengthening/ .... the rocks by the expansion,
until pieces break off. These broken-off pieces roll down steep slopes and form areas of
smooth/ .... rocks called potholes/ .... On steeper/ ....
slopes, the broken-off rocks lie around on the surface, forming rockeries/ ....

Q3.   Draw a set of three labelled diagrams to explain the following title:

<u>Physical weathering: Onion skin weathering in hot desert climates.</u>

Q4.   Briefly explain <u>two</u> ways in which <u>biological weathering</u> occurs.

....

....

....

....

Weathering

Q5. The following sentences describe chemical weathering in limestone areas. They are in the wrong order — write a) b) c) and d) in the gaps below to show the correct order.

a) In caves, the dripping water leaves deposits of insoluble calcium carbonate on the roof, forming stalactites, and on the floor, forming stalagmites.

b) This dissolves the limestone along lines of weakness, eg bedding planes and joints.

c) Rainwater absorbs carbon dioxide from the air and becomes weak carbonic acid.

d) These weaknesses are enlarged by solution, forming caves and swallow holes.

First sentence ......   Second sentence ......   Third sentence ......   Fourth sentence ......

Q6. Write a brief description of each of the following.

i) A limestone pavement

....

....

ii) A clint

....

....

iii) A gryke

....

....

Q7. Draw a diagram to show the features of a limestone area. Include <u>ten</u> features and label them.

Q8. <u>Chemical weathering</u> has an interesting effect on <u>granite</u>. What is the substance which is formed when granite is chemically weathered? Name an area where this substance is found.

....

....

Weather 'tis nobler to suffer the slings and arrows of outrageous limestone...

Remember weathering can be <u>physical</u> or <u>chemical</u>. You need to understand <u>both</u> for the exam and these questions cover all the details you'll need to know. Of course you'll be forever in my debt, but for now just make sure you can answer all the questions, or my hard work will be in vain.

Section Two — Rocks and Landscapes

The Hydrological Cycle

The hydrological cycle sounds pretty technical but remember 'hydro' just means water, so all it really means is <u>water cycle</u> — that sounds a lot easier.

Q1.   Complete the ten blanks in the paragraph below (the first letters are already filled in):

The hydrological cycle describes what happens to water on the planet. Over the sea, water e............................... into the air as w.................. v.................., which then r................ and c................, causing c........................ and the formation of c.................. Eventually, precipitation (e.g. r..........., s.................. or h................) falls.

Q2.   The labels are missing from this diagram. These labels are all the <u>processes</u>, such as "infiltration". Write in the correct words to complete the diagram.

1 ....

4 ....

5 ....

2 ....

6 ....

3 ....

7 ....

8 ....

Q3.   After a heavy rain over the River Severn basin, local people were told that the river would reach its highest level two or three days after the rain had stopped.

Explain why the river would not reach its highest level immediately after the rain. (Hint – you should use the words from Q2)

....

....

....

....

....

It's this water cycle Captain — most hydrological...

All this hydrological stuff is filled with loads of clever-sounding words like infiltration, percolation and wot not. But don't let that put you off, the actual ideas are pretty straightforward. Get them straight in your head and then learn the posh words to dazzle the Examiners.

Drainage Basins

Drainage basins are the areas near rivers. You'll need to know about their
main features and uses. Luckily for you here's a whole heap of questions.

Q1. What is a drainage basin?

....

....

Q2. A drainage basin can also be called the:

c ....

Q3. What is a watershed?

....

....

Q4. Look at the map of the Mississippi basin and complete the questions:

The Mississippi basin is the
world's second largest basin.

What is the largest?

....

a) St Louis is a major city built where two rivers (the .... and the
.........................) meet. This point is called a ....

b) The Ohio River flows into the Mississippi and is a branch, or ...., of it.

c) The river flows south into the Gulf of Mexico. Its end is called the ....
In fact, the Mississippi has several ends, because it has formed a delta.

d) The flow or <u>volume</u> of water passing along the river at any point is called the
d .... of the river. What else will the river be carrying?
Yes OK it will be carrying boats... but it will be carrying mud, sand, etc
that it has eroded, and this stuff is called s ....

Drainage Basins

Q5.   Look at this map. When it rains over this drainage basin, what will happen to the rainfall:

a) over A, the mixed woods?

....

....

b) over B?

....

....

c) over C?

....

d) over D?

....

e) over E?

....

Write down two other things that will affect how much water finally reaches point F.

....

....

Q6.   a) Describe three ways in which drainage basins are important or useful to people.
       Include examples.

....

....

....

....

....

b) Describe three problems that occur as a result of people living
    and working in drainage basins. Examples again please.

....

....

....

....

....

Drainage Basins

Q7. "River management" means planning how to use river basins; looking after the environment; measuring rainfall and water levels to try and reduce the effects of flooding. In Britain, the EA (The Environment Agency) and the Water Authorities (eg Severn-Trent Water) put lots of resources into river management.

Look at the map of the River Severn and answer the questions underneath:

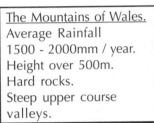

The Mountains of Wales.
Average Rainfall
1500 - 2000mm / year.
Height over 500m.
Hard rocks.
Steep upper course valleys.

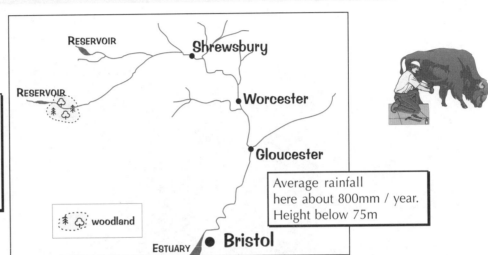

Average rainfall
here about 800mm / year.
Height below 75m

i) Give three reasons why the reservoirs are up in the mountainous part of the basin.

....
....
....

ii) Give two reasons why no dams and reservoirs are in the lower parts of the River Severn.

....
....

iii) What are the three main purposes of the reservoirs?

....
....

iv) The woodland areas are there as part of the river management.
Give three reasons why they are useful in the basin.

....
....
....
....

Brain drainage...

You don't just need the details of drainage basins themselves but also how they affect <u>people</u> — why are they important, how do people use them and all that jazz. Remember to throw in examples.

River Features of the Upper Stage

There's quite a lot of different river features to learn about, so for your learning ease they're split up into those from different stages of the river, starting with the upper...

Q1. Look at this diagram of the upper stage of a river and name the features (a, b, c, d) that are shown on it.

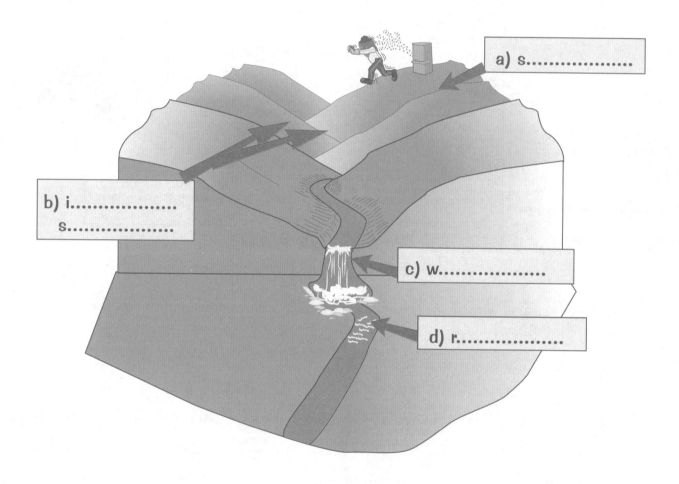

a) s.....................

b) i.....................
   s.....................

c) w.....................

d) r.....................

Q2. Finish off these sentences about upper stage rivers:

a) The main process that occurs in an upper stage river is ....

b) Interlocking spurs are caused when the river ....
....

c) Waterfalls occur where there is a layer of ....

d) The falling water wearing away at the foot of a waterfall forms a ....

<u>*River Features of the Upper Stage*</u>

Q3.   Look at the diagram of a waterfall. Briefly explain how
       waterfalls form and how their position changes through time.

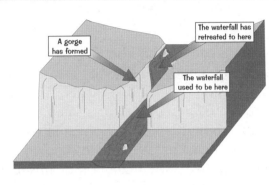

A gorge
has formed

The waterfall has
retreated to here

The waterfall
used to be here

....
....
....
....
....
....

Q4.   Name two famous waterfalls and say where they are.

....
....

Q5.   Rapids occur in the upper stages of the Colorado (USA) and
       Ardeche (France) and both of these are used for white water rafting.

       Write an explanation using labelled diagrams to show how rapids form.

River Features of the Middle Stage

Now the upper stage was good, but look at the middle stage
— a magnificent array of river features if ever I saw them...

Q1.   Correct this paragraph about the middle stage of a river
by circling the correct word(s) in each pair.

In the middle stage the river starts to wind and bend. These bends are called u-turns/
meanders. On the outside of each bend, the velocity is faster/slower, causing less/more
erosion here. This "sideways erosion" is called vertical/lateral erosion. The channel here is
deeper/shallower and the banks are eroded to form a steep slope called a gorge/river cliff.
On the inside of the bends, the current is slower/faster, the water is shallow, and erosion/
deposition occurs, creating little "beaches" of particles known as point bars/spits.
The winding of the meanders and their slow migration downstream, and the deposition of
mud, silt and other particles after floods, forms the flat land on either side of the river,
(known as the floodplain/scarp slope).

Q2.   Draw a labelled diagram to show the important features
of the middle stage of a river, as seen from above (aerial view).

Q3.   Label this diagram of a cross section of a meander, using the blank boxes:

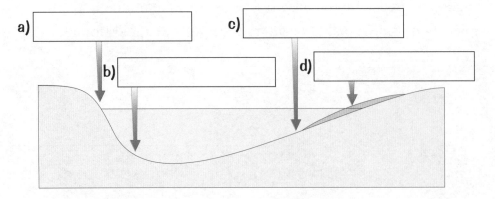

a)

b)

c)

d)

Q4.   Name two large, famous rivers which have meanders.

....

....

River Features of the Lower Stage

And last, but not least, the full glories of a river's lower stage...

Q1.   Give brief answers to the following questions:

a) In the lower stage of a river is the gradient steep or gentle?

....

b) What is the proper name for material deposited by the river?

....

c) What is the proper name for the wide valley floor?

....

d) What is the wide valley floor often used for?

....

e) Give two reasons why it is often used for this.

....

....

f) What is the name of the raised river banks formed from gravelly material deposited in floods?

....

g) Some rivers, such as the Thames, end in wide shallow mouths. What are these features called?

....

h) Other rivers, such as the Nile, split into several channels that lead to the sea.
    What are these channels called?

....

i) What is the name of the feature deposited at the sea by the channels in h)?

....

Q2.   There are many oxbow lakes on the River Amazon (Brazil) and the Mississippi (USA).
       Oxbow lakes can form in the middle or lower stages of a river.
       Add notes to the diagrams to explain how oxbow lakes form.

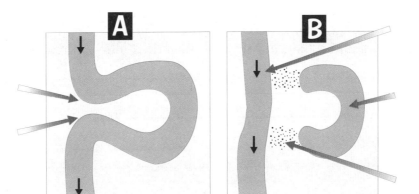

Impacts of Flooding

A major way rivers can affect people is flooding. Flooding always makes you think of disaster, houses washed away etc but flooding can also have good effects as well...

Q1. Floods can have both positive and negative impacts.

a) Write down two positive impacts, with examples.

....

....

b) Write down two negative impacts, with examples.

....

....

Q2. Look at the map of the Lynmouth flood disaster of 1952. Use this information and any other information you know to answer the questions below.

15-16 Aug 1952 up to 300mm of rain fell on Exmoor.

The previous two weeks had been very wet so the ground was already saturated.

Runoff was rapid and fast because slopes are steep on Exmoor, so the West and East Lyn Rivers filled up rapidly and overflowed.

BRISTOL CHANNEL N
Lynmouth
WEST LYN RIVER   EAST LYN RIVER
EXMOOR
over 300 m high

Estimated cost of damage to the town, the hotels, houses, possessions, was £9 million.

34 people died.

Erosion caused by the swollen rivers caused rocks, boulders and trees to collect and form temporary dams. When these collapsed huge waves of floodwater rushed down to Lynmouth.

a) What caused the floods?

....

....

....

....

b) What were the impacts of the floods?

....

....

....

....

Q3. Why does flooding often cause more problems in LEDCs (eg Mozambique in 2000) than in MEDCs? Give five different reasons.

....

....

....

....

....

Flood Management

Geography buzz words coming thick and fast — "management" is a good'n for talking about how people cope with hazards. After all, you can't stop floods but you can make plans to cope with them.

Q1.　Fill in the gaps in this paragraph about flood management.

River and flood management describes all the things that people do to try and have some control over rivers. Constant measuring and storage of past data allows us to p................ flooding more accurately. Water Authorities have made detailed maps of river basins showing the types of g.............. and s................. because these affect runoff. Weather stations also measure p.................... figures.

For example, in the Welsh Mountains the combination of much impermeable rock (eg slate), heavy rain and steep slopes means that after storms, lag times will be .... and runoff will be .... Hence flooding is ....

Q2.　Look at the diagram of a river basin which often floods. ❶❷and❸ indicate land uses. These land uses are making the flood problem worse.

Below each label, describe how you would change the land use and say how your changes would reduce the flooding.

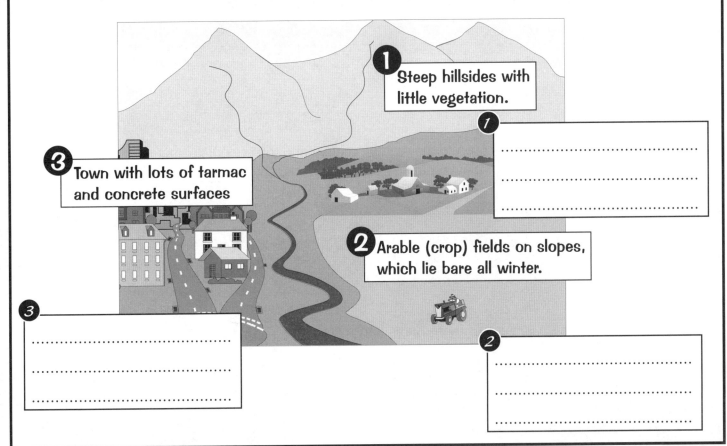

❶ Steep hillsides with little vegetation.

❸ Town with lots of tarmac and concrete surfaces

❷ Arable (crop) fields on slopes, which lie bare all winter.

Flood Management

Q3.   Look at the map of the River Rhone in France and then do the questions.

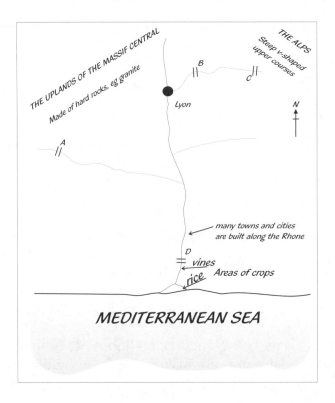

THE UPLANDS OF THE MASSIF CENTRAL
Made of hard rocks, eg granite

THE ALPS
Steep v-shaped upper courses

B

C

Lyon

N

A

many towns and cities are built along the Rhone

D
vines
rice   Areas of crops

MEDITERRANEAN SEA

i)   Give three reasons why dams have been built in the upper stages of the Rhone (at A, B, C).

....

....

....

ii) In the 300 km stretch from Lyon to the sea (the middle and lower course), there are twelve dams, eg at D, the Donzere Dam. Suggest three possible reasons why they have been built here.

....

....

....

iii) Explain two disadvantages of these dams and reservoirs.

....

....

....

Flood Management

Q4.   It is useful to know about river management in LEDCs too. Revise what you
know about the Aswan Dam in Egypt (River Nile). Then write down five
advantages of the creation of the Aswan Dam and five disadvantages of it.

ADVANTAGES ....

....

....

....

....

DISADVANTAGES ....

....

....

....

....

Q5.   Complete this paragraph by circling the correct word in the pairs.

> If a river floods often, engineers can deepen the channel — this is called
> sledging/dredging — to make it hold more water. A meandering river can
> be straightened (like the Mississippi has been). This causes the river to flow
> more quickly/slowly and take the water to the source/sea. Water can be
> diverted from one basin into another, or diverted into overflow channels, from
> a river where flooding is likely. Excess water can be diverted around the edge
> of towns in channels called relief channels/ring roads. In the Los Angeles basin
> excess water is diverted into large pools called spits/storage areas on the
> floodplain so that it can safely evaporate or infiltrate into the ground.

Flood management — get yourself an ark...

Flood management is a vital way people can cope with the dangers of flooding. You need to
understand the reasons why people live in flood risk areas and how they deal with this hazard.
Remember that all these flood management methods can be more effectively applied in MEDCs.

Measuring River Floods

By studying floods, we can monitor dangers and also help to predict future hazards.
But there's more to it than a pair of wellingtons and a ruler...

Q1.   The River Nile in Egypt used to flood every year, for several reasons. Look
      at the map and the unfinished notes in the boxes a) b) c) and d). Add some
      more explanation of your own to explain why you think flooding occurred.

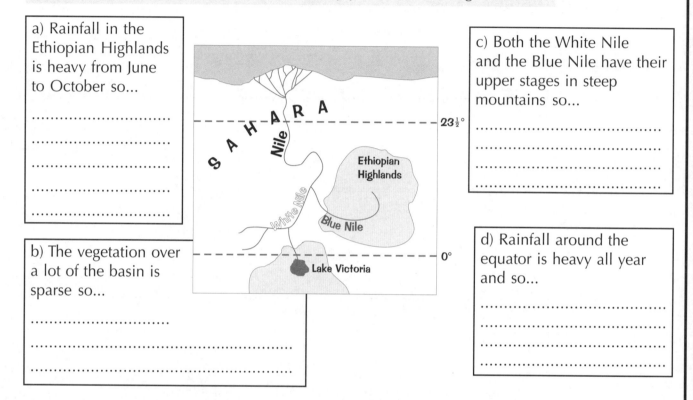

a) Rainfall in the
Ethiopian Highlands
is heavy from June
to October so...

....

....

....

....

....

c) Both the White Nile
and the Blue Nile have their
upper stages in steep
mountains so...

....

....

....

....

b) The vegetation over
a lot of the basin is
sparse so...

....

....

....

d) Rainfall around the
equator is heavy all year
and so...

....

....

....

....

Q2.   Correct the paragraph about the causes of flooding
      by circling the correct word in each pair.

As towns and cities grow larger, there are more and more areas of tarmac and concrete,
which causes runoff to decrease/increase, which leads to more/less flooding.
Also people often cut down trees (this is called afforestation/deforestation), which
increases/decreases the interception of the rainfall, and increases/decreases the runoff
into the rivers. Flooding is also more likely when there are areas of permeable/impermeable
rocks because the rain water cannot infiltrate/investigate into the ground. Another common
cause of flooding is snow melt, especially when this melt water runs down gentle/steep
valley sides into a river.

Q3.   What do we call a graph which shows the effect of one rain storm on the
      discharge (the volume of water flowing in cubic metres per second) of a river?

....

Section Three — Rivers

Measuring River Floods

Q4.   Look at this diagram. Name the parts of the diagram that are labelled 1 to 5.

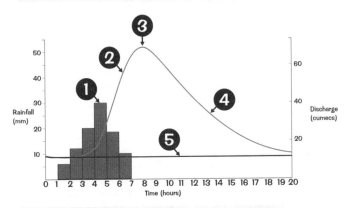

1 ....

2 ....

3 ....

4 ....

5 ....

Q5.   Briefly explain the following words:

a) Lag time

   ....

b) Base flow

   ....

Q6.   Look at the diagram in Q4. If the water authorities know that the river is
       full to the top of the banks when the discharge reaches 50 cumecs, does
       this graph predict that flooding will occur? (Tick the correct box)

   [ ] Yes   [ ] No

Q7.   When graphs like this are plotted for different storms, sometimes the graph
       can have a steep curve and sometimes it can be gentle, as in the diagrams below.

       In each column give five reasons why the graph may be this shape.

A steep hydrograph	A gentle hydrograph
1	1 ....
2	2 ....
3	3 ....
4	4 ....
5	5 ....

How deep is your flood — (is your flood, how deep is your flood)...

Run offs, lag times, base flows — lots of technical terms to learn here. But the basics are
that scientists can study flooding in order to <u>predict floods</u> and to make <u>plans</u> for the future.
Remember again that detailed studies are more often carried out in **MEDCs** than **LEDCs**.

Section Three — Rivers

Water Supply and Management

Flooding is a dramatic example of how rivers can affect people. But in the general course of our everyday lives we rely on rivers and other water supplies in many ways...

Q1. In Britain there is a huge and growing demand for water. Make a list of <u>ten</u> of the main uses of water. (Hints — uses in the home; in towns; in the countryside...)

1 .... 2 ....

3 .... 4 ....

5 .... 6 ....

7 .... 8 ....

9 .... 10 ....

Q2. Look at this map of Britain and answer the questions which follow:

Key   mm
over 1000
625 - 1000
under 625

UK rainfall

a) Name the 4 areas which have the highest input of rain water:

1 ....

2 ....

3 ....

4 ....

b) Give <u>two</u> reasons why these areas are not the ones with the greatest demand for water.

....

....

c) Describe the two ways that are used to try and even this out.

....

....

d) Describe <u>four</u> ways in which we could reduce our use of water.

....

....

....

....

Q3. In Britain we usually have more rainfall in winter. When is demand highest? Give three reasons for this high demand.

....

....

....

....

Section Three — Rivers

Water Supply and Management

Q4.   Describe the job that water authorities do in Britain.

....

....

....

....

....

....

Q5.   Write about four of the serious water supply problems in LEDCs.

....

....

....

....

....

....

Q6.   Correct this paragraph, by circling the right words from each pair:

<u>How LEDCs can improve their water supply and quality:</u>

In LEDCs, farmers are often taught and helped to dig wells. These schemes are
called self-service/self-help schemes. These wells can be lined with sand/concrete
to reduce/increase seepage and condensation/evaporation. The people are taught
how to keep their water unpolluted/polluted by keeping animal and human waste
away from fresh water supplies. Farmers are shown simple watering schemes
(called irritation/irrigation schemes), like spraying and drip-feeding/force-feeding
their crops.

Water supply — hilarious...
You need water for drinking and washing — 'tis one of the most fundamental requirements for all of
us. It's also one of the main difficulties in LEDCs where they often struggle to provide good healthy
water, if they have water at all. If you've done all the questions you'll know all this already.

The Power of the Sea

Buckets and spades and rubber rings are all well and good for seaside holidays but the sea can be a powerful force, which can shape the coastline. It can crush huge sand castles in a single bound.

Q1.　Look at this diagram and then answer the questions:

i)　What causes waves?

....

ii)　What is the top of a wave (①) called?

....

iii)　What is the bottom of a wave (②) called?

....

iv) If we measure the vertical difference between (①) and (②), what is this called?

....

v)　What is wave length?

....

vi) What happens to waves at ③, near the shore?

....

vii) What is the name for the forward movement of water up the beach?

....

viii) What is the name for the movement of water back down the beach?

....

ix) What is meant by the "fetch"?

....

x)　How does fetch affect wave size?

....

Q2.　Complete the table to show the difference between constructive and destructive waves:

	Constructive Waves	Destructive Waves
Type of weather		
Height		
Which is strongest, swash or backwash?		
Which processes are important? Erosion? Transport? Deposition?		

The Power of the Sea

Q3.   Name the four wave processes which erode the coast and explain them.

1.   ....
....
....

2.   ....
....
....

3.   ....
....
....

4.   ....
....
....

Q4.   What do we call the zigzag movement of pebbles along a beach caused by waves?

....

Q5.   Write out these four sentences in the right order:

a)   Each swash pushes particles up the beach at an angle.

b)   Therefore particles move along the beach and can pile up at the far end to form a spit.

c)   When the prevailing wind blows at an angle to the shore it causes the waves to approach at the same angle.

d)   Each backwash drags particles down the slope of the beach at 90 degrees to the shore.

1.   ....
....

2.   ....
....

3.   ....
....

4.   ....
....

The Power of the Sea

Q6. Draw and label a diagram to show the process described in Q5.

Q7. Label the four erosion features shown in this diagram:

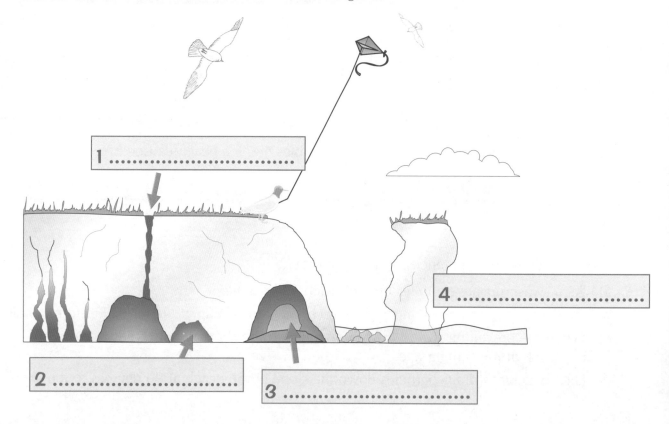

1 ....

2 ....

3 ....

4 ....

Q8. Correct the paragraph about the formation of cliffs
by circling the correct words in each pair:

On the coast, waves erode the rock between low tide and high tide/below low tide,
and create an undercut feature called a noose/notch. Eventually the rocks above are left
overhanging and unstable/stable, and they collapse, leaving a gentle/steep slope called
a cliff. The process starts again, and as the cliff keeps collapsing and retreating/advancing
a rocky surface, known as a concert platform/wave cut platform, is exposed at its base.

The Power of the Sea

Q9.   What factor causes some cliffs to be
       very steep and others to be very gentle?

       ....

Q10.   Write down "true" or "false" for each of these:

           Headlands form from harder rock.   ....

           Bays form from harder rock.   ....

           Name an example of a headland and an example of a bay.

           ....

           ....

Q11.   The Lulworth Cove area of Dorset has caves, blowholes,
       arches and stacks. Describe how these features form.

           Caves: ....

                         ....

           Blowholes: ....

                         ....

           Arches: ....

                         ....

           Stacks: ....

                         ....

Q12.   Complete this summary of coastal erosion:

           i) Name four types of coastal erosion.   ii) Name seven features created
                                                                 by coastal erosion.

           ....

           ....

           ....

           ....

Study the sea, sail through the exam — what a ship joke...

There are loads of processes to learn here — and loads of coastal features to remember.
But I reckon it's a darned good excuse to go to the beach for a field trip...

Coastal Deposition

The movement of the sea can deposit sand in distinctive patterns.
It can also deposit old boots and the occasional, unfortunate dozy whale.

Q1. i) One feature of deposition is a beach. Why do they often form in bays?
     ii) Name two types of particle that beaches can be made of.
     iii) What is a storm ridge? How does it form?
     iv) Name an example of a beach.

i. ....
....

ii. ....
....

iii. ....
....

iv. ....
....

Q2. Look at the map of Hurst Castle Spit, near Southampton.

Hurst Castle Spit

i) Does the prevailing wind blow from the south west or north east?

....

ii) Does longshore drift move particles to the west or to the east?

....

iii) What caused the spit to grow at point A?

....

iv) What do we call the "finger-like" ends of the spit (at B)?

....

v) What happens in the area of water C that is sheltered behind the spit?

....

vi) Name another example of a spit and say where it is.

....